PUZZLES and BRAIN TWISTERS

A FIRST BOOK

Puzzles and Brain Twisters

by Fred Walls

Franklin Watts, Inc.
730 Fifth Avenue
New York, N.Y. 10019

SBN 531-00693-X
SBN 531-02403-2 (pbk.)
Copyright © 1970 by Franklin Watts, Inc.
Library of Congress Catalog Card Number: 70-100096
Printed in the United States of America

6 5 4 3 2 1

CONTENTS

PUZZLES and BRAIN TWISTERS

PUZZLES WITH COINS

A Puzzle in Pennies

For this puzzle you need fifteen pennies — beans will do if pennies are not available.

Here is the puzzle you set. You place on the table 11 of the pennies, and challenge anyone to take away 5 from the 11, add 4, and leave 9.

Most people are tricked by the puzzle. They argue that if you take 5 pennies from 11, then 6 pennies are left. Add 4 to the 6, and the answer must be 10 — *not* 9.

But the answer can be 9. Work it out for yourself. If you have any difficulty, turn to the solution on page 54.

One Move at a Time

In this "checkerboard" puzzle, what you have to do is change the position of the checkers so that the blacks are in 5, 6, 7, and the reds are in 2, 3, 4. You must move the colors alternately — a red, then a black, then a red, and so on — you can only move to the next square; you are not allowed to "jump." You can move sideways, or up and down, or diagonally.

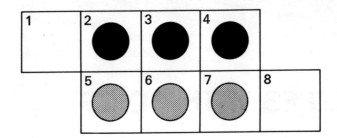

The puzzle can be solved in seven moves. See if you can do it in that number, then check your solution with the answer given on page 54.

Two Moves at a Time

Below you see 10 squares in a row, with black and red checkers or pennies and nickels laid out in alternate colors on squares 1 to 8.

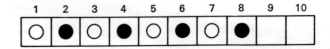

The problem is to get all the reds and all the blacks together by moving two disks at a time. When moving, you can jump over as

4

many others as you like — but you must always move two together, and keep them in the same order, so that if you move a black and a red together and the red is on the left, it must be put down on the left in the new squares.

You can solve the problem in only four moves, ending with the reds on squares 7 to 10 and the blacks on squares 3 to 6. It should not take you long to do it.

The solution appears on page 54.

PUZZLES WITH NUMBERS

A Magic Number Square

Here you see 9 squares arranged in rows of 3, with the numbers 1 to 9 marked in them.

The problem is to arrange the numbers so that no matter which way you add them up — across, downward, or from corner to corner — you will always get 15 as the total.

The answer is on page 55.

1	2	3
4	5	6
7	8	9

Hundreds and Hundreds!

1) Arrange the numbers 1, 2, 3, 4, 5, 6, 7, 8, and 9 so that they come to 100 exactly.
2) Arrange four 8's so that they will come to 100 exactly.
3) Now try to arrange four 5's in one line to make 100.
4) And finally, work out two ways of adding the figures 1, 2, 3, 4, 5, 6, and 7 together so that they come to 100 exactly.

The answers are on page 55.

"Think of a Number . . . !"

Ask somebody to think of a number (preferably less than 20, or the mental arithmetic becomes rather difficult).

Tell him to add 1.
Tell him to multiply by 2.
Tell him to add 3.
Tell him to multiply by 2 again.
Tell him to deduct 10.

Ask him for the answer, and after a mere second's thought you can tell him the number he first thought of.

How do you do it? By dividing the answer you are told by 4. This works for any number. Try a few for yourself and see.

"Think of Another Number . . . !"

Here is a think-of-a-number problem that mystifies most people.

Tell somebody to think of any number from 1 to 9.
Tell him to multiply it by 3.
Tell him to add 1.
Tell him to multiply by 3 again.
Tell him to add the number he first thought of.

7

You now tell him that the two-figure answer ends in the figure 3, and that if he takes that figure away he is left with the number he first thought of.

Try it out for yourself. You will find that it works every time.

A Tricky Subtraction

Can you subtract 45 from 45, and leave 45? It is easy when you know how.

The answer is on page 56.

Arranging Ones

Write six 1's in a row so that they total 15.

Then write them in another row so that they will total 24.

Check your answer on page 56.

Do These in Your Head

1. If four brothers with their wives each with two children met for tea, how many would there be in the party?
2. A class of boys stand in a long line. One boy is 19th in order from both ends. How many boys are there in the class?
3. When Tom was bicycling to town he met a man, his wife, two children and a dog. How many more legs than Tom had did he see on his way?
4. Mary is 16. In four years she will be twice as old as Jane was a year ago. How old is Jane?

Answers on page 56.

Find the Dates

The following is part of a letter that John wrote to his friend Peter on Sunday, April 28th.

8

"You left your jacket here last Friday. Perhaps you will call for it when you pass this way next Wednesday. I shall be going away next Friday."

See how quickly you can work out the answers to these questions and then turn to page 56 to see if you are right.

1. On what date was the jacket left behind?
2. Give the date when John was expected to call for his jacket.
3. On what date will Peter be going away?
4. In the year when the note was written, on what day of the week did May begin?
5. Give the number of days Peter expected the jacket to remain in his house.

Missing Numbers
A set of numbers in some sort of order like 2, 4, 6, 8, 10 or 12, 1, 11, 2, 10, 3, 9, 4 is said to form a series. A number is missing from each line below. What is it?
1. 3, . ., 9, 12, 15, 18, 21
2. 2, 7, 12, 17, 22, . ., 32
3. 30, 27, 24, 21, . ., 15, 12
4. 1, 2, 2, 4, . ., 6, 6, 8
5. 17, . ., 18, 15, 19, 14, 20, 13
6. 45, 36, 28, . ., 15, 10, 6
7. 2, 1, 3, 2, 4, . ., 5
8. 4, 9, . ., 25, 36, 49
9. 103, 204, 305, . . ., 507
10. 132, 243, 354, 465, . . .

Turn to page 56 to check your answers.

PUZZLES WITH MATCHES

These puzzles using matches are a lot of fun to work out on your own. They are also fun to do with your friends at parties.

When doing puzzles with matches, it is best always to use the "safety" kind, so that if one is dropped and stepped on there will not be any unfortunate accidents such as burning a hole in the carpet or starting a fire.

Match Squares
One form of puzzle with matches is to make squares of them, and then by moving some of the matches or taking some away, change the number of squares. Three such puzzles are set out on the next page.

Take 11 matches and arrange them in three squares as shown here:

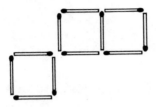

Now move three matches only, and leave two squares. All the matches must be used; you must not take any away.

Take 24 matches and arrange them into 9 squares as shown here:

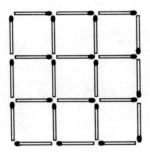

Now take away 8 of the matches and leave only two squares.

Arrange 12 matches into four squares, as shown in the diagram on the next page. The problem is to move four of these 12 matches so as to make only three squares. All the matches must be used; you must not take any away. The solutions are given on page 57.

11

Match Triangles

Take 18 matches and arrange them to make the following figure, which consists of 6 small triangles, 2 large ones, and a six-sided figure — a hexagon.

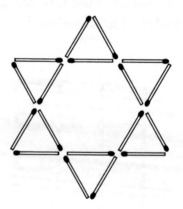

What you have to do is to move only two of the matches so as to leave yourself with 4 small triangles, 2 large ones, and 2 trapeziums — figures with two of their sides parallel.

The solutions are given on page 57.

12

WORD PUZZLES

Same Sound — Different Meanings

Have you ever thought what a large number of words there must be that have the same sound but different meanings? As an example, there are NIGHT and KNIGHT.

Below there are some clues to more words of a similar nature. If you have any trouble with them, turn to the solutions on page 58.

1 Look intently; leading to the next floor.
2 Seven days; feeble.
3 Manufactured; a young girl.
4 In a window; it hurts!
5 It is all around you; the eldest son.

13

6 A young lad; this floats.

7 An exchange of something for money; driven by the wind.

8 Letters in the post office; masculine.

9 Somewhat conceited; seen on a weathercock.

10 Just below your ribs; throw away something useful.

11 The sound of bells; on an orange.

12 Seven in a week; rather muddled.

13 Without any clothes; he likes honey.

14 Looks at; take forcibly.

The next three sets of clues are about words with the same sounds but three different meanings each.

15 A fruit; two together; you take the peel off the first one.

16 A source of metals; otherwise; used for propelling a boat.

17 One article of a kind; have on; at what place.

Hidden Names

In the squares at the top of the next page are hidden a number of names of various things. You have to find out what they are by working from square to square, going from right to left or left to right, upward or downward, or diagonally.

Here is a useful hint: when you have found one name in a group of squares, in nearly every case another name will begin in an adjacent square. In fact, if you can find the right name first, you can work through the squares one by one until you have found all the names. You use each individual letter only once — there is never any need to use a letter from any one square a second time.

The answers are on page 58.

P	A	T	E	L
E	A	N	P	O
R	E	H	E	O
T	G	T	N	X
I	E	R	A	P

5 Animals

O	N	S	R	O
B	N	I	M	E
O	L	R	A	M
N	D	A	D	R
O	N	P	D	I

5 Capital Cities

Making Words from Words

Here is an interesting game that you can either play by yourself or turn into a competition at your next party.

It is quite simple. All you have to do is select a word — preferably a fairly short one with at least two vowels and plenty of consonants — and see how many other words you can make from it using the letters it contains.

There are only two rules. The first is that, for each word found, you must use any letter in the original word only once; that is to say, if there is only one S in the original word, you could not use the S twice in the same word. The other rule is that all the words found must be real ones — made up words are not allowed.

When playing the game as a party competition, it is a good idea to set a time limit — say five minutes. The competitor who has found most words from the original word in that time is the winner.

15

And now for an example. A good word to pick is HISTORY. With very little thought, you can find at least 18 other words in it, as follows:

His, Story, Or, Toy, Tor, Rot, Is, Hit, Sir, Sort, Roy, Sit, Stir, Hist, Oh, Ho, So, To.

And now see what you can do with the word CAMBRIDGE.

Our list, for which we gave ourselves 5 minutes only, will be found on page 58.

Adding Words to Words

Quite a large number of words can be made into other words with entirely different meanings by the addition of a word. As an example, if you had the word HAT, you can turn it into HATRED by adding the word RED.

Below are some puzzles along the same lines. A word is given, followed by a double clue — one for the word to be added, and one for the final word. The word to be added has to be put after the given word in some cases, before it in others.

The solutions will be found on page 58.

1 FOR — add music to make a lot of money.
2 IN — add a taxi to make room on a ship.
3 PET — add a motor vehicle to make a floor covering.
4 DOCK — add something to write on to make a place in which to keep horses.
5 PET — add a baby dog to make an animated doll.
6 FARE — add something that cools you down to make a flourish of trumpets.
7 LET — add something you do with a knife to make a piece of meat.

16

8 ACE — add a friend to make a royal residence.
9 SOME — add part of a clock to make someone good-looking.
10 OR — add an adult male to make a big estate.

Mixed Syllables

The syllables of these words have been mixed up. Can you rearrange them so that each word in the left-hand column is correctly joined to those in the right-hand column?

You will notice, incidentally, that all the syllables are words in themselves.

The answers are on page 58.

BOW	WORD
HIT	PRESS
COW	IT
SUP	SPRIT
PASS	AT
CATCH	HER
NOT	ICE
DIG	SLIP
GO	AGE

Animal Endings

Quite a number of names of animals have endings that are words in themselves. For example, there is the word ON. If you add the letters LI to it, you get LION.

Can you find the names of the living creatures whose names end with the following words? There may be more than one answer:

17

1 KEY	5 HER	9 ALE
2 IMP	6 PINE	10 ROT
3 INK	7 USE	11 AT
4 RICH	8 ARK	12 OUT

The answers are on page 58.

Flower Endings

As in the case of Animal Endings, add letters to the following words to obtain the names of flowers.

1 ROCK	5 SLIP	9 IS
2 LIP	6 US	10 MARY
3 LION	7 LET	
4 ONE	8 HID	

The answers are on page 59.

Bird Endings

And here is a collection of birds, the names of which can be found in the same way.

1 CAN	4 BIN	7 ROW
2 KEN	5 OVER	8 RUSH
3 TIN	6 LOW	9 ON

The answers are on page 59.

Magic Word Squares

Have you ever tried making magic word squares — squares that read the same whether you read them across from left to right, or downward? You can see an example of one below.

E M I T
M A D E
I D E A
T E A R

You will notice right away that the first word is the same across or downward; the same with the second word; and the third; and the fourth.

See if you can make word squares from the following two sets of clues. The words are all of four letters in each case, of course.

1st Word Square: 1 Seen on a leopard.
                     2 Father.
                     3 Not closed.
                     4 For storing water.
2nd Word Square: 1 There are two on a bird.
                     2 A notion.
                     3 Tidy.
                     4 This usually opens into a garden.

The answers are on page 59.

In case you would like some more magic word squares for a party game, here are a few examples. You could make up your own clues, and set them as problems to your guests.

C A N T	B E N D	K I C K	N O N E
A R E A	E R I E	I C O N	O V E R
N E C K	N I B S	C O M E	N E A R
T A K E	D E S K	K N E E	E R R S

No Consonants

In each of the following words, the consonants have been replaced by asterisks. You should not have much difficulty in working out what the words are once you know that each of them is the name of a popular game or sport.

        1 * O O * * A * *
        2 * I * * I * *

```
3  *  A  *  E  *  A  *  *
4  *  E  *  *  I  *
5  *  *  I  I  *  *
6  *  *  A  *  I  *  *
```
The answers are on page 59.

Palindromes

Do you know what a palindrome is? It is a word that is spelled the same way no matter whether you go from left to right or right to left. An example is the girl's name ADA.

Here are some clues to other palindromes. Remember that the answers are all single words that can be spelled the same forward or backward. Answers on page 59.

1 When you address a lady.
2 This road is quite flat.
3 Twelve o'clock, midday.
4 You see with this.
5 This sheep is a female.
6 A baby wears this at feeding time.
7 After the sun has gone down; also a girl's name.

Words to Reverse

Unlike palindromes, there are some words that, when spelled backward, make other words with entirely different meanings. As an example: SAW when spelled backward becomes WAS.

Here are some clues to other words that can be reversed. In each set, the first clue refers to the word spelled from left to right; the second clue refers to the word spelled in the reverse direction. Answers on page 59.

20

1 An unpleasant rodent; black and sticky.
2 Not good; a small fish.
3 A kind of seaman; an island in the Mediterranean Sea on which Napoleon was exiled.
4 Very cosy; these go off with a loud bang.
5 Very bad indeed; not dead.
6 Not off; not yes.
7 Cease moving; these go with pans.
8 You could score a home run with this; look inside the collar of your jacket.
9 Count all your fingers and thumbs; some curtains are made of this.
10 Coal comes from this; tilt.

The Cat Game

This is both a puzzle and a game for a party. The idea is to think of words beginning with the letters c-a-t. For example, if somebody says: "This Cat is a list of things for sale," the answer is "Catalog."

Here are some more Cats for you to think about — and to try on your friends when you have discovered the answers. As a check they are given on page 60.

1 This CAT is a means of throwing stones.
2 This CAT is a disaster.
3 This CAT is a way of getting a batter out.
4 This CAT is a supplier of food.
5 This CAT is a butterfly grub.
6 This CAT is a herd of cows.
7 This CAT is the church of a bishop.
8 This CAT is the name of a girl, and of a great queen.

Word Chains

In a word chain start with a word — a short one of four or five letters — and by altering only one letter at a time change into another word.

For example, start with the word BOOT and end with the word SHOE by changing only one letter at a time. It is a strict rule that when you change a letter, the word you make must be a real one, and not something quite meaningless. So to make a start:

BOOT

SOOT (B changed to S)

SHOT (1st O changed to H)

SHOE (T changed to E)

Thus BOOT has been changed into SHOE in three moves.

Try the following four word chains:

1 Change COLD into MELT in 4 moves.
2 Change SEAS into LAND in 4 moves.
3 Change MAKE into MEND in 5 moves.
4 Change BITE into FOOD in 6 moves.

You will find the answers on page 60.

The Zoo Game

Although this is really a word puzzle, it is a very old favorite as a competition game at parties. All you have to do is to jumble up the letters of some easily remembered animals seen at the zoo, set them down on paper, and give your guests five minutes to work out what they are.

Eight or ten animals would be quite enough, and below is a list for you to choose from. The answers are given on page 60.

1	NILO	11	RNOOCAC
2	OXF	12	GRAUJA
3	REED	13	GANKOORA
4	ERAB	14	THANERP
5	CLAME	15	PELETHAN
6	KNASE	16	NEUPING
7	GRITE	17	RAGEFIF
8	BRAZE	18	TRULET
9	KNOMEY	19	THROSIC
10	DREENIRE	20	PACKECO

Anagrams

If you take the letters of a word and rearrange them to make a different word, you have made an anagram.

As an example, start with the word TEA. Very little thought will show you that you can rearrange the letters to make the word EAT. Thus EAT is an anagram of TEA; alternatively TEA is an anagram of EAT.

Anagrams are a very popular kind of word puzzle, and you will find various examples — some easy, some quite difficult — in certain newspapers and magazines. Here are a few simple words to practice on. In each case the word and the clue to the anagram are given.

1 LEAP. Think of church bells.
2 NAME. The long hair down the neck of a horse.
3 APE. A green vegetable.
4 ARM. Spoil.
5 TRAP. Not the whole of anything.
6 ARMY. A girl's name.
7 TIME. Very tiny.

8 STAGE. Entrances to a field or garden.

9 LINE. A great river in Africa.

10 BAKER. Used to bring vehicles to a halt.

You will find the answers on page 60.

Changing Words

Can you change BACK into LINE in four moves, changing one letter in each move and making a new word each time?

Here are some clues to help you.

1. A place to keep money.
2. Cause of ruin.
3. Narrow road.

The word sequence is on page 60.

Mixed Words

Mixing up two words gives some curious results, even though you keep all the letters of each word in their proper order. As an example, if you mixed the words CAT and DOG you could get, say, CADTOG or DOCAGT.

Here are some more mixed words. The clues given should enable you to unravel them quite quickly.

1. Remove the animal, but leave his house.
   SPITYG
2. Remove the parent, but leave the child.
   MOBATHBERY
3. Remove the bird, but leave the flower.
   SPRIPAMRRROOSEW

24

4. Remove the continent, but leave the ocean.

PAECURIOFIPCE

The solutions are on page 60.

Alphabetical Order

If you arrange the letters of any word in alphabetical order, it can look very strange indeed — even though it may be very familiar when spelled the right way.

Here are the names of some very ordinary objects around the home that have had their letters arranged in this way. If you are sitting indoors, you can see some of them around you.

Can you find out what the words are? Clues are given to help you. The answers are on page 60.

ABELT (You eat at this).

ACHIR (You sit in this).

EFIR (Warming during winter days).

ALMP (Very necessary when it gets dark).

AIRSST (You use these to get to the top floor).

ABHT (Do you like yours hot or cold?).

CEHIKNT (The room where the cooking is done).

GHILT (Also very necessary when it gets dark).

ADEGNR (A place for flowers and vegetables).

EFLORSW (They look nice in vases).

Figures for Letters

If you substitute the figures, 1, 2, 3, 4, 5, 6, 7, and 8 for the letters of a certain word, and use those figures for the letters of other words, here are some of the results you could get —

3678 (The king of beasts).

1278 (Not long now).

3215 (Mislaid).

5263 (Hard work).

148 (It makes the day warm).

863 (Nothing).

245 (Not in).

845 (You have to crack this).

See if you can find what letters the figures stand for, using the clues to help you. Having worked out the words fitting the clues, you will then be able to find the word the figures 1, 2, 3, 4, 5, 6, 7, and 8 stand for. The solution is quite easy if you have your wits about you. It is to be found on page 61.

Rearranging Letters

There are quite a number of words that, if you rearrange their letters, will make other words. As an example, if you started with the word END, you could by using exactly the same letters — no letter to be used twice, of course — make it into DEN and NED; but you could not make it into EDEN because you would be using the E twice when there was only one in the original word.

Here are ten words that you can turn into other words in exactly the same way. The clues will help. You can check your answers by turning to page 61.

1. GOAT (The Romans wore this long ago).
2. LIED (They say this of anyone who is very lazy).
3. FELT (Not right).
4. MATE (Describes a number of people who do things together).
5. ROVE (Across the top of).

26

6. RING (Kind of smile).
7. CAPES (Astronauts travel in this).
8. THORN (A compass points in this direction).
9. SHORE (You still see this pulling carts).
10. PEACH (Not in the least expensive).

Two Words in One

Have you ever noticed that some words can be split into two entirely separate words, each separate word having a meaning quite different from the original?

A good example is in the first line of the paragraph above — the word NOTICED divides into NOT and ICED.

A few more examples are: AM-END; AT-ONE; CAN-DID; BE-HAVE; NOT-ABLE.

Below are eleven sets of clues. Each set consists of a clue to the first half of a word, a clue to the second half, and a clue to the whole word. Remember that the two halves of the whole word are complete words in themselves.

See if you can find the words.

1. Not on; the finish; annoy
2. A private motor vehicle; a domestic animal; a soft floor-covering.
3. A grown-up male human; a long time; control or direct.
4. Two short of a dozen; an insect; the occupant of a rented house.
5. Fighting between nations; a study; a sort of caretaker.
6. A problem in arithmetic; a girl's name; a sort of précis.
7. A male offspring; used for catching fish; a kind of poem.
8. Slang for nonsense; you did this to your breakfast; turn around and around.

9. The organ of hearing; a bird's home; sincere or serious.
10. Made with a knife; a girl; a weapon.
11. A narrow bed of canvas; 2,000 pounds; a lightweight cloth.

The answers, and some further examples for use in a party game, are to be found on page 61.

Three Things to Drink
Can you, in half a minute, name three things to drink that end in the letter A?
Three are named on page 61.

Heads and Tails
There are quite a number of words that can be turned into other words just by adding one letter to the beginning or to the end, and sometimes by doing both.

Here is a simple example. Start with the word HE. Add T to it, and you get THE. Add N to it, and you get HEN. Add both the T to the front and the N to the end, and you get THEN.

See what you can do with the following words assisted by the clues given.

1. ARC (Add a letter to each end and get a tree).
2. TO (Add a letter to each end to mean halt).
3. EAT (Add a letter to the beginning to mean tidy).
4. TAR (Add a letter to each end to mean begin).
5. INNER (Add a letter to the beginning to mean a meal).
6. FIR (Add a letter to the end to get something warming).
7. ATE (Add a letter to the beginning to mean not early).
8. THIN (Add a letter to the end, and the answer is what you are having to do now).

28

9. OWL (Add a letter to the beginning to mean an awful noise).

You can add one letter to the beginning and one letter to the end of each of the following words to make other words. Clues to the other words are given. Can you work out what they are?

10. EIGHT (Rather heavy).
11. TAR (Look hard at something).
12. PAR (Not together).
13. LIE (A foreigner).
14. HANG (A lot of small coins are called this).
15. OR (Either a stronghold, or a kind, according to the letter you put first).
16. ONES (Quite the reverse of cheating).
17. ONE (Cash).
18. ROW (This is what a wolf does).

The answers are on page 61.

The answers are on page 61.

Now for Some Cans
This is both a puzzle and a game for a party. The idea is to think of words beginning with the letters C-A-N. For example, if somebody says: "This Can is a member of the Commonwealth," the answer is "Canada."

Here are some Cans for you to think about — and to try on your friends. Turn to page 61 to see if you have guessed correctly.

Turn to page 61 to see if you have guessed correctly.

1. This can contains water.
2. This can is a bird.
3. This can crosses something out.
4. This can gives light.
5. This can is very doggy.

6. This can makes a very loud noise.
7. This can floats.
8. This can is a place to obtain food.

And Lastly, Some Ages

This is a little more difficult than Cans, because it is the ending of words you have to think about. All the words referred to in the clues end in AGE.

1. This age is the end of anger.
2. This age is the end of a barrier.
3. This age is the end of a treatment for sprains.
4. This age is the end of something rather narrow.
5. This age is the end of something on wheels.
6. This age is the end of a place where plays are performed.
7. This age is the end of a wise man.
8. This age is the end of something found in a book.
9. This age is the end of something earned.

The answers are on page 62.

The Same Sound

There are many words that have a different meaning and a different spelling but sound the same. For example, STEEL and STEAL.

Can you find other words from the following clues?

1. A blood vessel; conceited.
2. Part of a window; something that hurts.
3. Lacking color; holds water.
4. Foot of some animals; rain heavily.
5. Being able to see; place on which a building stands.
6. Part of shoes; to get better.

7. To post a letter; a boy or man.
8. Grows on the head; an animal.

You can check your answers on page 62.

Same Spelling — Different Meaning
Now here are some clues to words that are spelled the same way
but have different meanings. Turn to page 62 to see if you have
found the right words.

1. Not dark; just.
2. A long piece of wood; to fasten with gum.
3. Refuse to work; to hit.
4. Healthy; a deep hole with water in it.
5. A building to store money in; the side of a river.
6. The front of your body; a big strong box.
7. The time when something happens; a sweet, brown fruit.
8. To make a vehicle go; a path that leads to a house.
9. Covering on a tree trunk; the sound a dog makes.

BRAIN TWISTERS

Can You Read This Poem?

> 2YSUR
> 2YSUB
> ICUR2YS4me!

The answer is on page 62.

Look at Your Phonograph Records!

How many grooves has each side of a 12-inch long-playing record?

The answer is on page 62.

Why Tuesday?

Read what follows, and see if you are as quick-witted as John.

John saw in a newspaper that there was to be a big display of jet airliners in a month's time. Unfortunately the place where it was to be held was a good twenty-five miles away, and rather awkward to get to because there were no trains or buses going direct.

But John's father wanted to see the display as well, so he took John along to the local garage proprietor to arrange to hire a car.

"H'm!" said the garage proprietor, who prided himself on being something of a wit. "That week's a bit difficult. You see, on Monday I have to take a group to the beach. On Tuesday I have to turn out for old Mrs. Jones's funeral. Wednesday's my day off, and Thursday is market day — I'm always booked up then. Friday and Saturday I have to be here for the weekend visitors. It looks as though I can't take you at all that week, sir."

John's father looked disappointed, but John just grinned.

"Right," he said. "We'll go on Tuesday."

The garage proprietor grinned back. "I see you're no fool, young feller," he said. "Tuesday it is!"

Now why was John so sure about that particular day?

You will find the answer on page 62.

Crossing the River

A farmer had to cross a river one day with a dog, a sheep, and a bale of hay, but the only boat he had was so small that he could get only an animal or the hay into it besides himself.

The trouble was, if he left the dog alone with the sheep, the dog would attack it; and if he left the sheep alone with the hay, the sheep would eat it.

33

How does the farmer manage to avoid these mishaps and yet get himself, the animals, and the hay across the river?

The answer is on page 62.

The Five Rabbits

Five rabbits were playing in a field. A farmer came along and shot one dead. How many rabbits remained in the field?

The answer is on page 63.

The Rope Ladder

A rope ladder hangs over the side of a ship so that it just reaches the water. Its rungs are 9 inches apart. How many rungs will be underwater when the tide has risen 3 feet?

The answer is on page 63.

A Problem with Jugs

Supposing you wanted exactly 7 pints of water, but the only jugs you had were a 3-pint size and a 5-pint size. How would you set about getting the 7 pints accurately?

It is no good filling both jugs, and trying to pour out 1 pint by guesswork — 7 pints exactly is the order!

The answer is on page 63.

Weights, Scales, and Potatoes

Here are two problems with weights, scales, and potatoes. The first is quite easy; the second is rather more difficult.

If you want to try to work out the problems by actually weighing, and you have not enough room for bulky things like potatoes, use rice; and instead of lb. weights, use oz. weights.

Problem 1: With only the 1-lb. and the 3-lb. weight, weigh out 10 lb. potatoes into 2-lb. lots.

Problem 2: With only the 2-lb. and the 3-lb. weight, weigh out 16 lb. potatoes into 4-lb. lots.

The answers are on page 63.

In One Line Only

Cover this page with some thin tissue paper and see if you can draw the figure below in one line, without raising your pencil off the paper, and without drawing along any line a second time.

The solution is given on page 64.

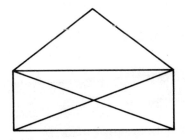

The figure on the next page is rather more difficult. It consists of two squares inside a circle.

The same rules apply — you have to draw the complete figure in one line, without lifting your pencil from the paper once, without going over any line twice, and this time without crossing any line either.

The solution is on page 64.

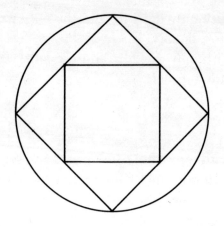

Seven Conundrums

1 "As I was going to St. Ives
I met a man with seven wives.
Each wife had seven bags;
Each bag had seven cats.
How many were going to St. Ives?"

2 In ran four legs;
Snatched up one leg.
Out rushed two legs;
Picked up three legs;
Threw them at four legs.
Out rushed four legs, and
Two legs got back one leg.
   What do all these legs refer to?

3 If John's father is Henry's son, what relation is John to Henry?

4 Some boys were going into school. There was one boy in front of two boys, one boy behind two boys, and one boy between two boys. How many boys were there?

36

5 What is it that is bought by the yard and worn by the foot?
6 To what question can you truthfully answer nothing but "yes"?
7 What is it that occurs once in a minute, twice in a moment, yet not at all in a week?

The answers are on page 64.

Simplified Spelling

Spell the word "expediency" in five letters. The answer is on page 64.

Selling the Land

Jones said to Smith: "I think I'll sell that piece of land at the bottom of my garden, but I can't make up my mind how much to ask for it. What do you suggest?"

"Well," said Smith, "what are its dimensions?"

Jones drew the following diagram and handed it over.

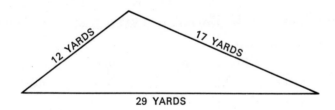

Smith studied the drawing for a second or two, then passed it back. "If your dimensions are right, you won't get so much as a dime for it," he said laughing.

Now why did he say such a surprising thing as that?

The answer is on page 64.

The Tail of a Dog

Here is a neat little poser that will catch most people if they do not know the dodge already:

Which has the most tails — one dog or no dog?

You'll find the solution on page 64.

How Many Times?

John, Jack, Jim, and Joe all decided to take up horse-riding. Jim went twice as many times as Jack, and John went four times more than Joe but three times less than Jim.

Joe went 15 times altogether.

How many times did Jack go?

Turn to page 65 for the answer.

The Teacup Mystery

Here is a neat little puzzle that you could try out on your friends. It baffles most people — until they know the simple secret.

You need three cups and ten lumps of sugar. The puzzle is to put the ten lumps into the three cups so that there is an odd number of lumps in each cup.

It seems impossible at first sight. Supposing, for example, you put 1 lump in the first cup, and 5 lumps in the second — you would then have 4 lumps in the third cup, and 4 is an even, not an odd, number. In fact, if you put odd numbers of lumps of any amount in two cups, you always seem to have an even number left over for the third cup.

Of course, there is a catch in the problem. Think it out for a minute or so — you should be able to discover how to work it out.

Turn to page 65 for the answer.

Which Limb Was It?

Here is a test of wits.

Dick and his sister Mary were reading a letter — very neatly written as usual — from their brother James, who was away at school.

"I've had a bit of an accident," James wrote. "It's nothing serious. I fell off my bike yesterday and badly sprained a limb. I came down with an awful wallop, and saw stars — there must have been a brick in the road or something. Well, no more for now, because I must run to catch the mailman."

"Pooh, what a silly letter!" exclaimed Mary. "He doesn't even bother to say which limb he has sprained."

"Use your brains!" retorted Dick "He's as good as told us."

And if you are told that James was in every respect normal, do you know too? You ought to after just a moment's thought.

The answer is on page 65.

Figure It Out

"Good gracious!" said Jack, as he looked at his evening paper. "One of the compositors has been having a little joke."

John looked at the newspaper, and this is what he saw.

"1234516 378249 after 854 minute, but 64493 3885 equalized. There was 58 further 37824, 159 the game 45949 in 1 draw."

"I see what's happened," said John. "He's put numbers instead of letters. All we have to do is put the letters back — it will be the same letter each time the same number occurs."

John and Jack soon put things right. Can you do the same? If so, you will be able to read the report of the match.

Answer on page 65.

39

North and South

Two people were standing facing opposite directions, yet each could see the other without turning around. Why was that?

The answer is on page 65.

Dividing up the Chocolate

Six boys were given a bag containing six bars of chocolate. The boys divided up the bars one to each boy, yet at the end one bar still remained in the bag. How was that?

The answer is on page 66.

What Am I?

1. I have four legs but I cannot walk on them. I have a back but I cannot bend it. When you want me to move I cannot do it myself. And yet people find me of great use.

2. I have a tongue but cannot speak. Most people look down on me when I am in the street and yet they find me useful. This is because they rely on me to keep them dry and warm.

3. I can touch you but you will never see me. When all is still and quiet I am never about, but everyone knows when I am on the move. Then I feel strong and you know I am coming.

4. I am not alive though I can nod and smile. I like to do what you do but often it seems to be just the opposite. When you turn your back on me I disappear from your sight.

Answers on page 66.

Colored Marbles

I have three bags of colored marbles, red, blue, yellow, and green. There are as many colors in the first bag as in the second, but the second has a color that is not in the first. The third bag has one color and it is in neither of the other bags.

If I want to keep as many colors as possible, which bag can I give away?

Answer on page 66.

Nine Conundrums
1. What is it that has a mouth that is bigger than its head?
2. If you burn this tree down, you are left with it. What kind of tree is it?
3. What kind of man can truly be said to be immersed in his work?
4. What kind of tables do people eat?
5. What is the difference between foggy weather and a man?
6. When is a rock not a rock?
7. What can you knit without knitting needles or wool?
8. What is the center of gravity?
9. What vegetable is dangerous when found in a ship?

The answers are on page 66.

How Old Are They?
Jim is four years younger than his brother Bill, but in five years' time Bill will be twice as old as Jim is now. How old are Jim and Bill now?

Check your answer on page 66.

Find the Odd Word
In each of the following groups of words there is one that is odd man out. For example, in the first group all are the names of trees

except *tulip,* which is a flower, so that is the odd word. Now do the others and turn to page 66 to check your answers.

1. Elm, oak, tulip, ash, poplar.
2. Hat, coat, trousers, umbrella, scarf.
3. Red, blue, green, yellow, paper.
4. Swim, fly, run, sit, slide.
5. Sun, earth, candle, lamp, taper.
6. Chair, table, stool, bench, couch.
7. Ham, mutton, beef, lard, pork.
8. Road, avenue, street, square, lane.
9. Potato, apple, pear, plum, peach.
10. Car, train, engine, bus, streetcar.
11. Salmon, rod, crab, flounder, herring.
12. Horse, turkey, cow, pig, donkey.
13. Handkerchief, purse, bag, basket, pocket.
14. Soldier, sailor, airman, farmer, policeman.
15. Trumpet, violin, bugler, flute, guitar.
16. England, France, Paris, Germany, Spain.
17. Tea, brandy, coffee, milk, cocoa.
18. Peas, cabbage, beans, tomatoes, sprouts.
19. Kitten, puppy, cub, foal, ass.
20. Chuckle, groan, smile, laugh, titter.

OPTICAL ILLUSIONS

Can you always believe what you see? At first thought you would probably answer yes, but after you have looked at some of the diagrams on this and the following pages, you will begin to wonder.

In the first place, did you know that all people with normal vision have one so-called blind spot in each eye? If you do not believe it, then hold this page up level with your eyes, close the right eye, and look at the right-hand spot with the left eye.

●   ●

If the page is about twelve inches or so from your face, you will probably be able to see both dots. Now move the page slowly nearer. At about ten inches or so, the left-hand dot will have disappeared. Now try it the reverse way — close the left eye, and look at the left-hand spot with the right eye. The same thing happens.

It is nothing to be alarmed about, of course. The explanation is that the whole of the back of your eye (the retina) is sensitive to light except in one place — where the main eye nerve joins the eye from the brain.

Verticals and Horizontals

Things that are vertical nearly always give the illusion of being more important than things that are horizontal. As an example, a vertical line seems longer than a horizontal one of the same length. To test this look at the diagram below, and guess which is the longer line. The vertical one, you think? Measure them both.

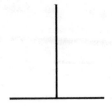

Divided lines seem longer than lines that are not divided. Look at the following drawing, and decide which is the longer — the part of the line that is divided, or the part that is not? Again, test with a ruler.

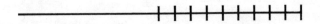

A row of dots gives the same illusion. In the diagram below, which is the greater distance — from the left-hand end of the row of dots to the right, or from *that* dot to the far right-hand one?

• • • • • • • • • •   •

Arrow heads can be very misleading too. In the next diagram, which part of the line would you say was the longer — the left-hand part or the right-hand part? Again, your ruler will give you the answer.

Which is the greater distance in the following diagram — from points 1 to 2, or from points 2 to 3?

A Problem in Perspective
And now for a very peculiar illusion. In the drawing on the next page you see three figures walking down a long passage.

Which of these three figures is the biggest? The back one, you think? Your ruler will soon demonstrate to you that they are all practically the same size.

45

The explanation is that you *expect* the figures to get smaller from front to back because figures farther away always look smaller in real life. The "farther away" effect has been created by the lines that represent the passage, for they are drawn to a point of "perspective," just as you would see a point of perspective if you looked down a long, perfectly straight road — it would seem to disappear at a point in the far distance.

To make the figures in the diagram look the same size to you, the artist would have to draw them getting smaller from the front to the back — in fact, he would have to make the rear figure only about a quarter of the height of the front one.

If you are any good at drawing, try some out on your friends. Optical illusions nearly always mystify people.

Some Illusions with Squares
Going back to what was said about vertical things seeming to be more important than horizontal things, here is an illusion with squares that is based on the same principle. Which of the two following squares is larger, the left-hand one or the right-hand one? You will find out if you measure them.

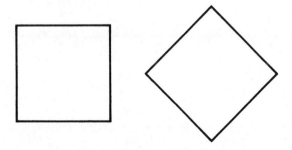

The next diagram shows a white square in a black square, and a black square in a white square. To most people, light-colored things always seem larger than dark-colored things.

Now, looking at the two inside squares, which would you say was the larger — the white square or the black one?

An illusion that is somewhat similar is demonstrated in the next diagram. Have you ever noticed that when you see an object surrounded by much larger objects, the first object seems quite small by comparison? Yet if it were surrounded by smaller objects it would seem quite large.

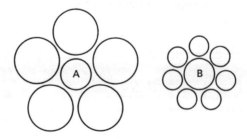

Now look at the above diagrams. Which would you say was the larger circle — A or B?

Lines That Cross

When lines cross other lines, the eye is usually deceived by trying to follow the two sets of lines simultaneously.

Would you say that the figure inside the circles is a true square?

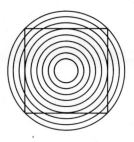

Again, are the vertical lines in the next figure parallel with one another? And are they straight?

Yet again, are the lines making up the big V in the next diagram really straight? They look as though they are drawn in a series of steps, and some people would say that they look twisted.

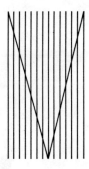

And for a real puzzler, try to discover in the next diagram which line, AC or BC, would be the continuous one if it were joined through the horizontal lines.

Do not forget to check each of the diagrams with a ruler. You will be surprised at some of the results.

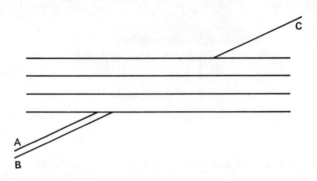

The Mysterious Gray Spots

The next diagram is of quite a different character. If you hold the book up level with your face and about 12 inches from your eyes, you will not only see a number of black squares, but some gray spots in the corners where the squares meet.

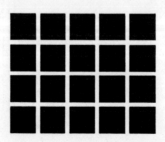

Now try to look directly at one of the gray spots. It promptly disappears — but you can see other gray spots out of the corners of your eyes. Now try to look at another of these gray spots. That too promptly disappears.

The Revolving Circles
Here is a diagram of a lot of circles.

If you hold up the book at eye level and move it about with a circular motion, the circles will seem to go around in the direction in which you are moving the book. The explanation is that your eye tends to go just a little faster than the book, giving an impression of forward motion. If you reverse the direction of the circular motion of the book, the circles will seem to go around in the opposite direction.

The Two Boxers

Here is a little device that is very easy to make and which is really a simple form of cinema. All you need is a disk of cardboard about one and a half inches in diameter and some elastic.

Make some holes in the cardboard at opposite sides. Then draw on the cardboard two figures to represent boxers — rather like the ones you can see here.

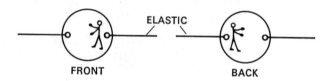

FRONT   BACK

Be careful to get their positions right, because if you put them on sides of the cardboard opposite to the sides shown here the result will look somewhat silly when you come to make the device work.

The drawings done, thread elastic through the holes, tie the ends of it to some kind of support so that it is just beginning to stretch, and then "wind up" the cardboard by turning it over and over. When it is wound up enough, let go and watch the figures on the cardboard. They will appear to be boxing each other with considerable vigor!

The explanation is that your eyes have what is called "persistence of vision." This means that they go on "seeing" an object for a very short time after they can no longer actually see it. So if you have two objects that constantly appear before your eyes and just as constantly disappear again, your eyes will go on seeing each of them while still looking at the other.

That is the reason why, when you look at either one side of the card or the other when it is not spinning, you see only one figure, but if you set it spinning on its elastic, you can "see" both figures at the same time.

The same principle is made use of in the movies and in television. In the movies a number of "still pictures" (that is, photographs) are made to appear before your eyes in rapid succession — so rapid that when a new picture is on the screen before you, you are still "seeing" the previous one. As each picture is slightly different from the one before it, you have the illusion of movement.

In television, a tiny spot of light rushes across the screen at terrific speed, and your eye goes on "seeing" it long after it has left one place on the screen for the next. It is made to vary from light to dark as it goes, according to the scene you are viewing, and so you get the illusion of a picture.

SOLUTIONS

PUZZLES WITH COINS

A Puzzle in Pennies
Put the 11 pennies on the table, and separate 5 from them. Add the 4 pennies to the 5 — not to the 6 left behind and you have 9.

One Move at a Time
One solution is: 2 to 1; 6 to 2; 4 to 6; 7 to 4; 3 to 7; 5 to 3; 1 to 5.

Two Moves at a Time
The solution is as shown in the diagrams on the next page. The moves are:

2 and 3 to 9 and 10; 5 and 6 to 2 and 3; 8 and 9 to 5 and 6; and 1
and 2 to 8 and 9.

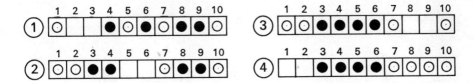

PUZZLES WITH NUMBERS

A Magic Number Square

2	9	4
7	5	3
6	1	8

Hundreds and Hundreds!

1) Add $1 + 2 + 3 + 4 + 5 + 6 + 7$ to 8 times 9 — the answer is
   100.

2) $\frac{8}{.8} \times \frac{8}{.8}$ Any other number similarly arranged will also come
   to 100.

3) $(5 + 5) \times (5 + 5) = 100$.

4)

15	32
36	57
47	6
2	4
——	1
100	——
——	100
	——

A Tricky Subtraction

987654321   (totals 45)

123456789   (totals 45)

864197532   (totals 45)

Arranging Ones

$1 + 1 + 1 + 1 + 11 = 15.$ $1 + 1 + 11 + 11 = 24.$

Do These in Your Head

1. 16; 2. 37; 3. 10; 4. 11.

Find the Dates

1. April 26th; 2. May 1st; 3. May 3rd; 4. Wednesday; 5. 5.

Missing Numbers

1. 6; 2. 27; 3. 18; 4. 4; 5. 16; 6. 21; 7. 3; 8. 16; 9. 406; 10. 576.

PUZZLES WITH MATCHES

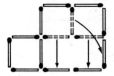

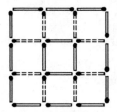

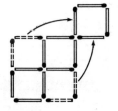

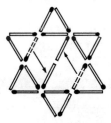

WORD PUZZLES

Same Sound — Different Meanings
1. Stare; stair. 2. Week; weak. 3. Made; maid. 4. Pane; pain. 5. Air; heir. 6. Boy; buoy. 7. Sale; sail. 8. Mail; male. 9. Vain; vane. 10. Waist; waste. 11. Peal; peel. 12. Days; daze. 13. Bare; bear. 14. Sees; seize. 15. Pear; pair; pare. 16. Ore; or; oar. 17. Ware; wear; where.

Hidden Names
5 Animals: Ape; Antelope; Ox; Panther; Tiger. *5 Capital Cities:* Bonn; London; Paris; Rome; Madrid.

Making Words from Words
Cam, Bridge, Bride, Ridge, Gem, Bread, Cab, Cad, Cadge, Age, Are, Mad, Madge, Mace, Bed, Bid, Bad, Ram, Rage, Bird, Dram, Drab, Drag, Cram, Crab, Crib, Grim (and the 5 minutes was up!)

Adding Words to Words
1. For-tune. 2. Cab-in. 3. Car-pet. 4. Pad-dock. 5. Pup-pet. 6. Fan-fare. 7. Cut-let. 8. Pal-ace. 9. Hand-some. 10. Man-or.

Mixed Syllables
Bowsprit. Catchword. Hither. Notice. Cowslip. Digit. Suppress. Passage. Goat.

Animal Endings
1. Monkey, Donkey, Turkey. 2. Shrimp. 3. Mink. 4. Ostrich. 5. Panther. 6. Porcupine. 7. Mouse. 8. Shark. 9. Whale. 10. Parrot. 11. Cat. 12. Trout.

58

Flower Endings

1. Shamrock. 2. Tulip. 3. Dandelion. 4. Anemone. 5. Cowslip.
6. Crocus. 7. Violet. 8. Orchid. 9. Iris. 10. Rosemary.

Bird Endings

1. Pelican. 2. Chicken. 3. Martin. 4. Robin. 5. Plover. 6. Swallow.
7. Sparrow. 8. Thrush. 9. Heron.

Magic Word Squares

S P O T	W I N G
P A P A	I D E A
O P E N	N E A T
T A N K	G A T E

No Consonants

1. Football. 2. Fishing. 3. Baseball. 4. Tennis. 5. Skiing. 6. Skating.

Palindromes

1 Madam	5 Ewe
2 Level	6 Bib
3 Noon	7 Eve
4 Eye	

Some more palindromes are: Toot; Tenet; Dud; Pup; Refer;
Deified; Sees; Gag; Minim; Anna; Deed; Peep; Dad; Pop; Nun.

Words to Reverse

1 Rat; Tar	6 On; No
2 Bad; Dab	7 Stop; Pots
3 Able; Elba	8 Bat; Tab
4 Snug; Guns	9 Ten; Net
5 Evil; Live	10 Pit; Tip

The Cat Game
1. Catapult. 2. Catastrophe. 3. Catch. 4. Caterer. 5. Caterpillar.
6. Cattle. 7. Cathedral. 8. Catherine.

Word Chains

1	COLD	BOLD	BOLT	BELT	MELT	
2	SEAS	LEAS	LENS	LEND	LAND	
3	MAKE	MANE	LANE	LAND	LEND	MEND
4	BITE	MITE	MINE	MIND	FIND	FOND	FOOD

The Zoo Game
1. Lion. 2. Fox. 3. Deer. 4. Bear. 5. Camel. 6. Snake. 7. Tiger.
8. Zebra. 9. Monkey. 10. Reindeer. 11. Raccoon. 12. Jaguar. 13.
Kangaroo. 14. Panther. 15. Elephant. 16. Penguin. 17. Giraffe.
18. Turtle. 19. Ostrich. 20. Peacock.

Anagrams
1. Peal. 2. Mane. 3. Pea. 4. Mar. 5. Part. 6. Mary. 7. Mite. 8. Gates.
9. Nile. 10. Brake.

Changing Words
BACK — BANK — BANE — LANE — LINE

Mixed Words
1. Pig, sty. 2. Mother, baby. 3. Sparrow, primrose. 4. Europe,
Pacific.

Alphabetical Order
Table. Chair. Fire. Lamp. Stairs. Bath. Kitchen. Light. Garden.
Flowers.

Figures for Letters
Lion, Soon, Lost, Toil, Sun, Nil, Out, Nut. The original word represented by the figures is: Solution.

Rearranging Letters
1. Toga. 2. Idle. 3. Left. 4. Team. 5. Over. 6. Grin. 7. Space. 8. North. 9. Horse. 10. Cheap.

Two Words in One

1.	OFF-END	7.	SON-NET
2.	CAR-PET	8.	ROT-ATE
3.	MAN-AGE	9.	EAR-NEST
4.	TEN-ANT	10.	CUT-LASS
5.	WAR-DEN	11.	COT-TON
6.	SUM-MARY		

Further Examples
Ban-king; Bar-bed; Bat-ten; Bob-bin; Bran-dish; Cap-size; Cross-bar; Den-ounce; Ham-let; Hum-or; Mat-tress; Pal-let; Sat-in; Spar-row; Wan-ton.

Three Things to Drink
Tea, cocoa, soda (there are others).

Heads and Tails
1. L-ARC-H. 2. S-TO-P. 3. N-EAT. 4. S-TAR-T. 5. D-INNER. 6. FIR-E. 7. L-ATE. 8. THIN-K. 9. H-OWL. 10. W-EIGHT-Y. 11. S-TAR-E. 12. A-PAR-T. 13. A-LIE-N. 14. C-HANG-E. 15. F-OR-T or S-OR-T. 16. H-ONES-T. 17. M-ONE-Y. 18. P-ROW-L.

Now for Some Cans
1. Canal; 2. Canary; 3. Cancels; 4. Candle; 5. Canine; 6. Cannon; 7. Canoe; 8. Canteen.

And Lastly, Some Ages
1. Rage; 2. Barrage; 3. Massage; 4. Passage; 5. Carriage; 6. Stage;
7. Sage; 8. Page; 9. Wage.

The Same Sound
1. vein, vain; 2. pane, pain; 3. pale, pail; 4. paw, pour; 5. sight,
site; 6. heel, heal; 7. mail, male; 8. hair, hare.

Same Spelling — Different Meaning
1. fair; 2. stick; 3. strike; 4. well; 5. bank; 6. chest; 7. date; 8. drive;
9. bark.

BRAIN TWISTERS

Can You Read This Poem?

> Too wise you are
> Too wise you be
> I see you are too wise for me!

Look at Your Phonograph Records!
Only one — it starts at the outside edge, and goes on and on until it
reaches the middle.

Why Tuesday?
Whoever heard of a funeral being arranged a month in advance?
The garage proprietor was trying to pull John's leg.

Crossing the River
The farmer first takes over the sheep and leaves it.
  He then returns, fetches the dog, leaves the dog and takes back
the sheep.

62

He leaves the sheep and takes over the hay. He leaves the hay with the dog.

He then returns and brings over the sheep.

There is another solution — the farmer takes the hay on the second trip. You can work out the rest of the journeys for yourself.

The Five Rabbits

Only one rabbit — the dead one. The others would have been scared away by the shot.

The Rope Ladder

None of the rungs will be underwater — the ship, and hence the rope ladder, will rise with the tide.

A Problem with Jugs

To measure out exactly 7 pints having only a 3-pint and a 5-pint jug, proceed as follows:

1 Fill the 5-pint jug.
2 From it fill the 3-pint jug and pour this away, leaving just 2 pints in the 5-pint jug.
3 Pour the 2 pints into the 3-pint jug, and fill up the 5-pint jug.

Result: 2 pints + 5 pints = 7 pints.

Weights, Scales, and Potatoes

1 Put the 1-lb. weight into one pan, and the 3-lb. weight into the other. The difference must be 2 lb., so weigh out the 2-lb. lots into the pan containing the 1-lb. weight.

2 (a) Put both weights into one pan, and weigh out two 5-lb. lots, leaving 6 lb. over.

(b) Now put the weights into separate pans, and weigh 1 lb. of potatoes from each of the 5-lb. lots. Result: 2 lots of 4 lb. each.

(c) Take all the weights off the pans.

(d) Put the two 1-lb. lots of potatoes together into one pan, and balance them with 2 lb. from the 6-lb. lot. Result: another two lots of 4 lb. each, making 16 lb. potatoes divided into four 4-lb. lots.

In One Line Only
S = Start
F = Finish

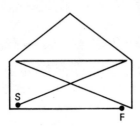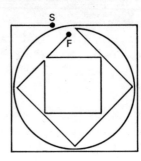

Seven Conundrums

1 Only one — all the others were coming away from St. Ives.
2 A dog, a leg of lamb, a butcher, and a three-legged stool.
3 His grandson.
4 Only three —in single file.
5 Stair carpet.
6 "What word do the letters Y E S spell?"
7 The letter M.

Simplified Spelling
XPDNC

Selling the Land
Any two sides of a triangle must, when added together, be greater than the third. On the dimensions given, Jones had no land at all to offer, but only a straight line.

64

The Tail of a Dog
One dog has one tail, no dog has two tails — therefore no dog has one more tail than one dog.

How Many Times?
Jack went riding 11 times.

The Teacup Mystery
Having divided out the lumps of sugar so that two cups have an odd number of lumps and the third has an even number, stand one of the cups with an odd number of lumps inside the one with an even number, and you will have complied with the terms of the puzzle — all the cups will have an odd number of lumps in them.

Which Limb Was It?
If James had to run to catch the mailman, he couldn't have the sprain in one of his legs. Bad sprains are painful, and he couldn't run if he had one. Since he was their brother, both Dick and Mary would know whether he wrote right-handed or left-handed. His letter was "very neatly written as usual," remember; so he had not sprained his writing arm.

You were told that James was in every respect normal, and from that you would be correct in deducing that he wrote with his right hand. Therefore it was his left arm that he had injured.

Figure It Out
Arsenal scored after one minute, but Leeds soon equalized. There was no further score, and the game ended in a draw.

North and South
They were facing each another.

Dividing up the Chocolate
The boy who was given the last bar was given it inside the bag.

What Am I?
1. A chair; 2. A shoe; 3. The wind; 4. Your reflection in a mirror.

Colored Marbles
This is a trick question. The answer is none of them, of course!

Nine Conundrums
1. A river.
2. An ash.
3. A deep-sea diver.
4. Vegetables.
5. One is mist; the other is Mister.
6. When it is a shamrock.
7. Your brows.
8. The letter V.
9. A leek (leak).

How Old Are They?
Bill is thirteen and Jim is nine.

Find the Odd Word
1. Tulip; 2. Umbrella; 3. Paper; 4. Sit; 5. Earth; 6. Table; 7. Lard; 8. Square; 9. Potato; 10. Engine; 11. Rod; 12. Turkey; 13. Handkerchief; 14. Farmer; 15. Bugler; 16. Paris; 17. Brandy; 18. Tomatoes; 19. Ass; 20. Groan.